Hal Leonard Student Piano Library

Piano Lessons

BOOK 4

FOREWORD

When music excites our interest and imagination, we eagerly put our hearts into learning it. The music in the **Hal Leonard Student Piano Library** encourages practise, progress, confidence, and best of all – success! Over 1,000 students and teachers in a nationwide test market responded with enthusiasm to the:

- variety of styles and moods
- natural rhythmic flow, singable melodies and lyrics
- "best ever" teacher accompaniments
- improvisations integrated throughout the **Lesson Books**
- orchestrated accompaniments included in audio and MIDI formats.

When new concepts have an immediate application to the music, the effort it takes to learn these skills seems worth it. Test market teachers and students were especially excited about the:

- "realistic" pacing that challenges without overwhelming
- clear and concise presentation of concepts that allows room for a teacher's individual approach
- uncluttered page layout that keeps the focus on the music.

The **Piano Practice Games** books are preparation activities to coordinate technique, concepts, and creativity with the actual music in **Piano Lessons**. In addition, the **Piano Theory Workbook** presents fun writing activities for review, and the **Piano Solos** series reinforces concepts with challenging performance repertoire.

The **Hal Leonard Student Piano Library** is the result of the efforts of many individuals. We extend our gratitude to all the teachers, students, and colleagues who shared their energy and creative input. May this method guide your learning as you bring this music to life.

Best wishes,

Authors
Barbara Kreader, Fred Kern,
Phillip Keveren

Consultants
Mona Rejino, Tony Caramia,
Bruce Berr, Richard Rejino

Director,
Educational Keyboard Publications
Margaret Otwell

Editor
Carol Klose

Illustrator
Fred Bell

To access audio, visit:
www.halleonard.com/mylibrary

Enter Code
7928-0332-1912-9154

ISBN 978-0-634-08426-3

HAL•LEONARD®

Visit Hal Leonard Online at
www.halleonard.com

World headquarters, contact:
Hal Leonard
7777 West Bluemound Road
Milwaukee, WI 53213
Email: info@halleonard.com

In Europe, contact:
Hal Leonard Europe Limited
1 Red Place
London, W1K 6PL
Email: info@halleonardeurope.com

In Australia, contact:
Hal Leonard Australia Pty. Ltd.
4 Lentara Court
Cheltenham, Victoria, 3192 Australia
Email: info@halleonard.com.au

REVIEW OF BOOK THREE

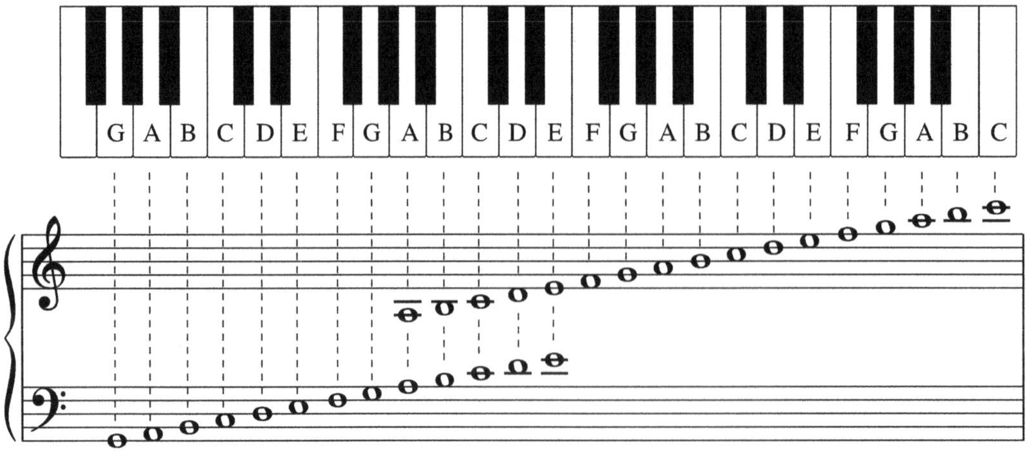

NOTE VALUES

quavers
two quavers fill the
time of one crotchet

dotted-crotchet quaver pattern
fills the time of two crotchets

INTERVALS

Interval of a 6th 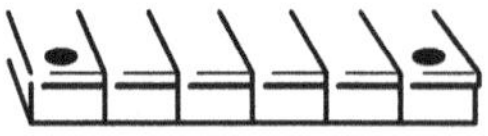

semitone
the distance from one key to
another, with no key in between

tone
the distance from one key to
another, with one key in between

FIVE-FINGER PATTERNS

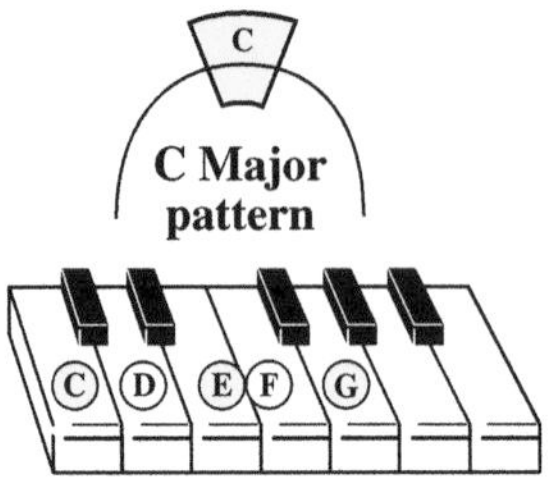

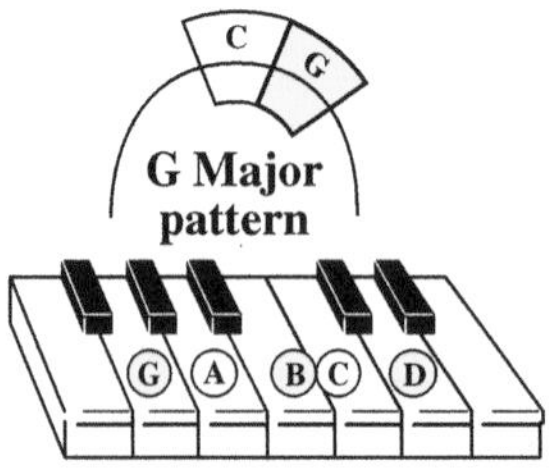

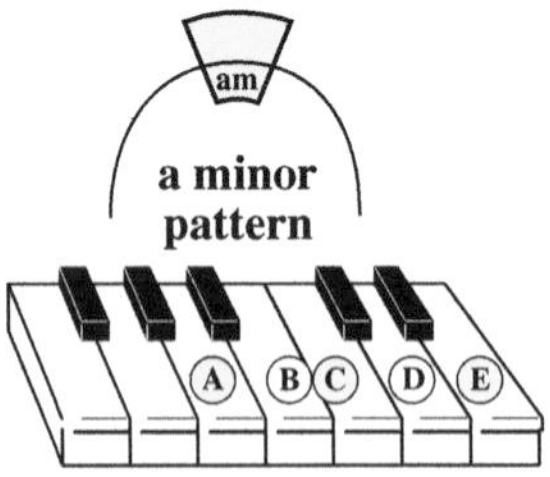

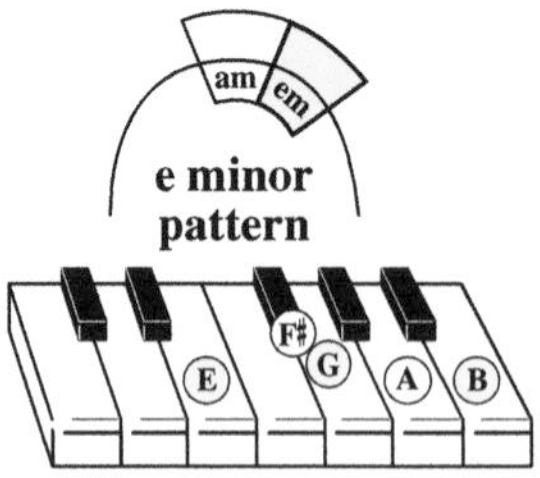

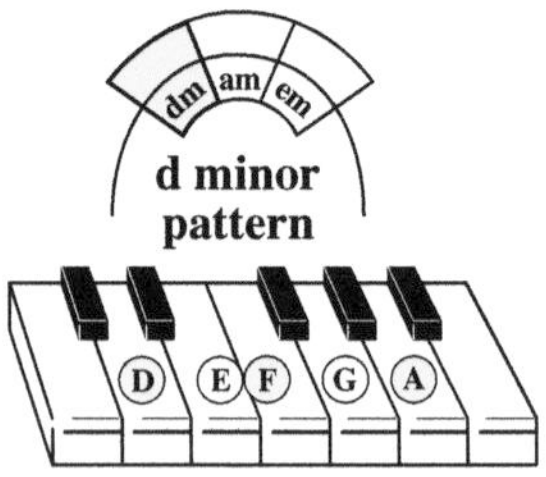

MUSICAL TERMS

time signature 2/4  two beats fill every bar
the beat is a crotchet

loco — play the notes where written

a tempo — return to the original tempo

D.S. (Dal Segno) al Fine — return to 𝄋 (*segno*) and play to the end (*fine*)

D.C. (Da Capo) al Coda — return to the beginning and play to the first coda sign 𝄌; then skip to the next coda sign 𝄌

15ma — play two octaves higher than written

CONTENTS

UNIT 1 RELATED FIVE-FINGER PATTERNS

PLAYING IN C MAJOR & A MINOR

UNIT 2 EXPLORING THE SCALES

UNIT 3 DISCOVERING THE PRIMARY TRIADS

PLAYING IN G MAJOR & E MINOR

UNIT 4 EXPLORING THE SCALES

UNIT 5 DISCOVERING THE PRIMARY TRIADS

** Students can check pieces as they play them.*

Related Five-Finger Patterns

Every major five-finger pattern has a related minor five-finger pattern.

To find the related minor pattern:

1. Play the major pattern with your L.H.
2. Place your R.H. thumb one tone above the highest note of the major pattern.
3. Play the minor pattern with your R.H.

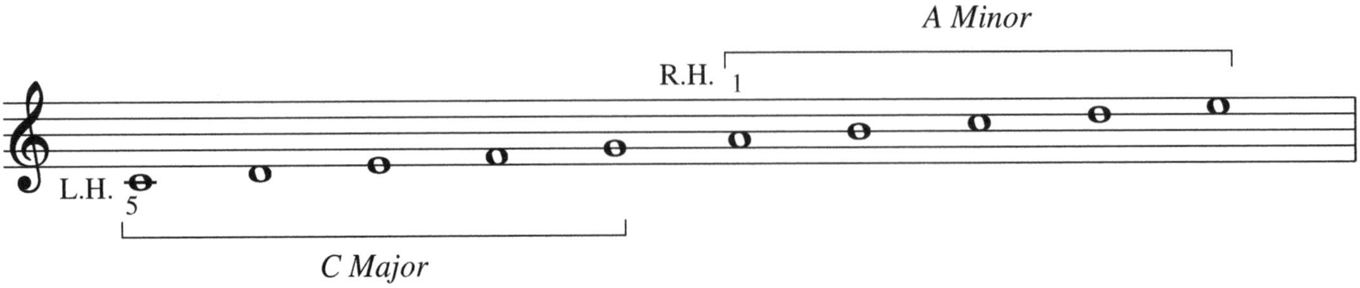

My Own Song
in C Major & A Minor

As you listen to the accompaniment, improvise a melody using the **C Major** pattern with your L.H. and the **A Minor** pattern (relative minor) with your R.H. Begin playing in the C Major pattern. Your teacher will tell you when to change to the A Minor pattern.

Accompaniment (Student improvises one octave higher than shown above.)

Flowing (♩=120)

Rustic Dance

Barbara Kreader

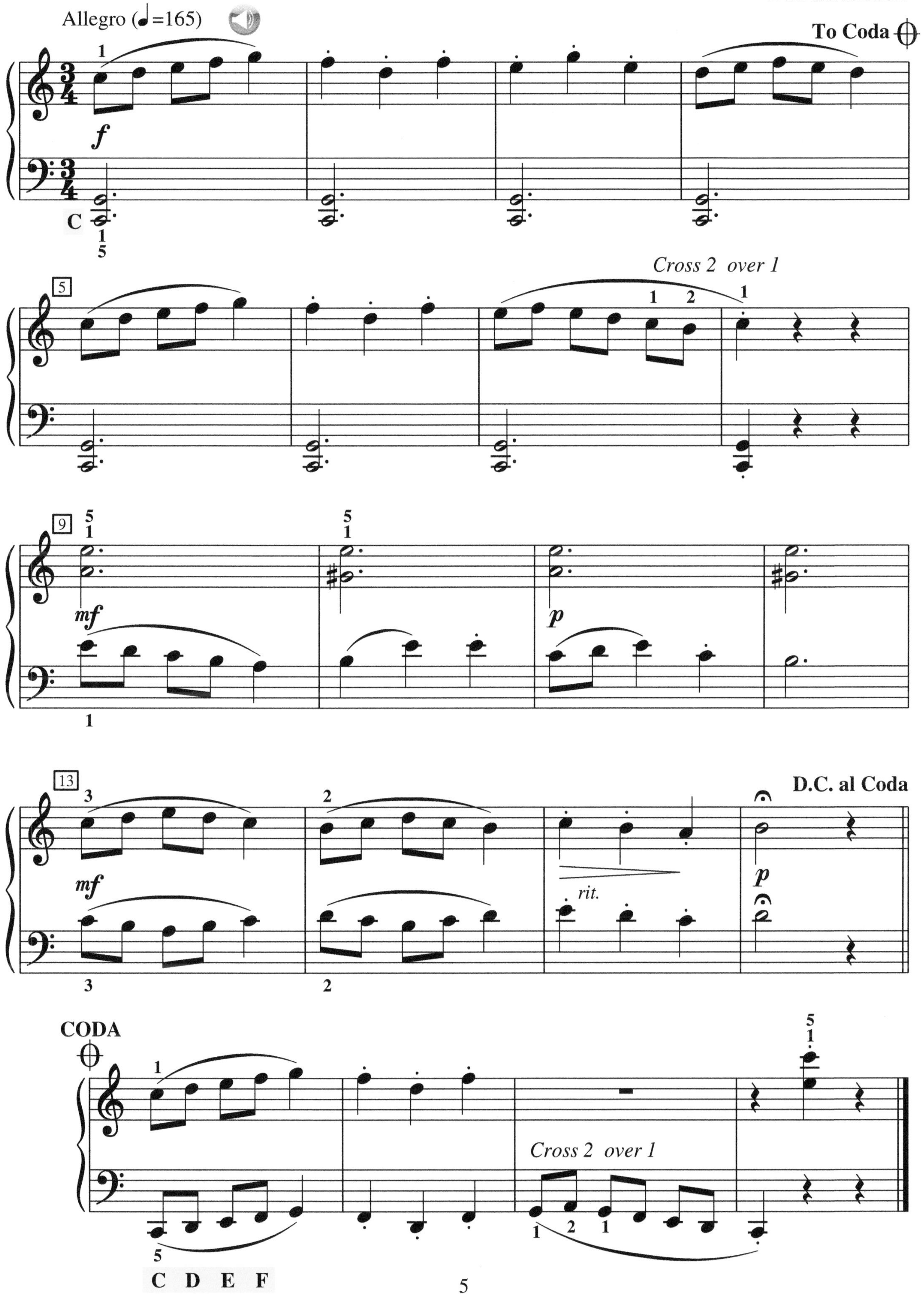

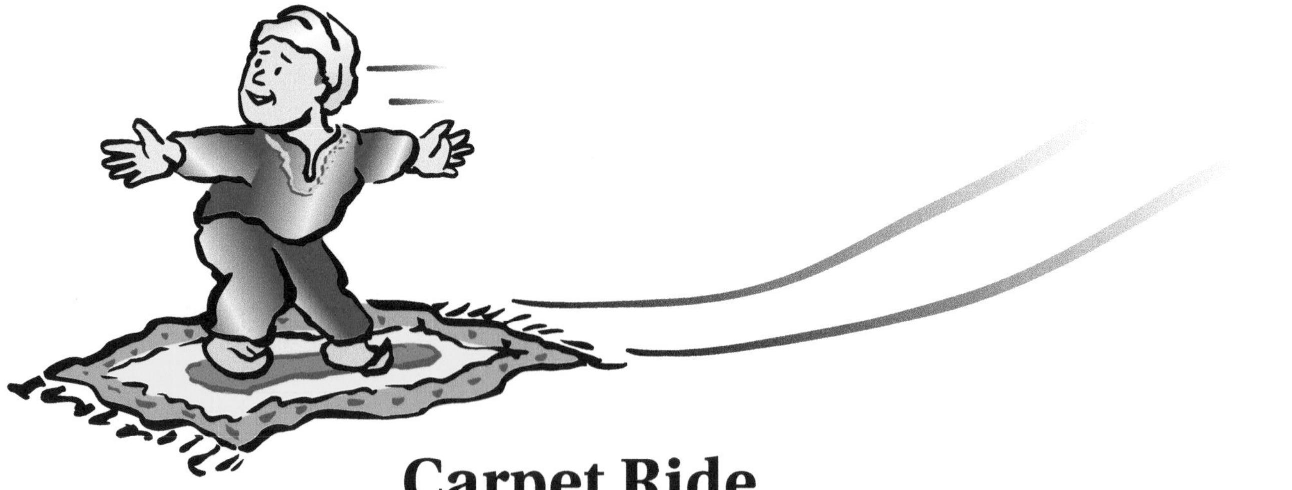

Carpet Ride

Mysteriously (♩=135)

Phillip Keveren

G & Em

My Own Song
in G Major & E Minor

As you listen to the accompaniment, improvise a melody using the **G Major** pattern with your L.H. and the **E Minor** pattern (relative minor) with your R.H. Begin playing in the G Major pattern. Your teacher will tell you when to change to the E Minor pattern.

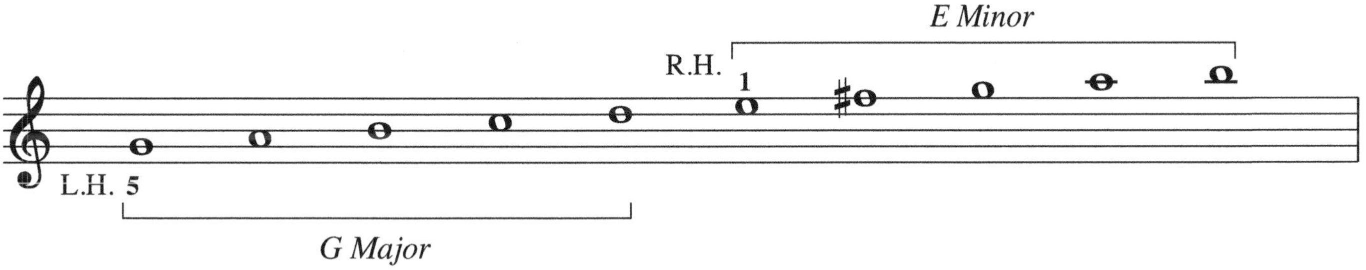

Accompaniment (Student improvises one octave higher than shown above.)

Bouncy (♫ = ♩♪ triplet) (♩=130)

QUAVER REST

A **Quaver Rest** fills the time of one quaver.

SYNCOPATION

Music becomes **syncopated** when the rhythmic emphasis shifts to a weak beat – either ahead of or behind the strong beats in the bar.

Clap and count these patterns:

Mister Banjo

Creole
Arranged by Phillip Keveren

Spirited (♩=170)

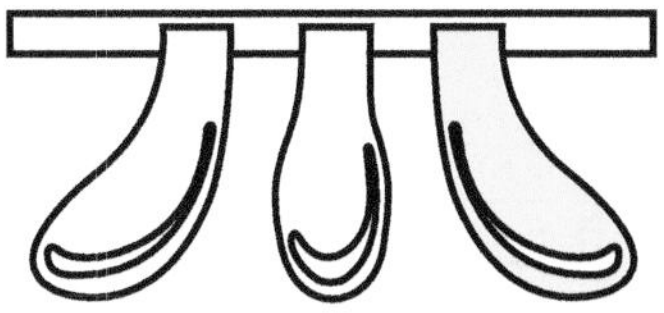

SYNCOPATED PEDALLING

When you press the sustain pedal, the notes will continue to ring after you release the keys. To produce a smooth sound, release and press the pedal quickly. Always keep your heel on the floor.

Change the sustain pedal **immediately after** playing the notes. Pedalling too late will cause the sound to blur; pedalling too early will cause a break in the sound.

Morning Bells

With energy (♩=135)

Phillip Keveren

INTERVAL of a 7th

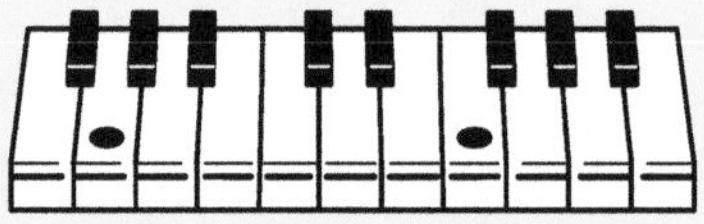

On the piano, a 7th
- skips five keys
- skips five letters

On the stave, a 7th skips from either line to line or space to space and skips five letter names.

Ribbons

Smoothly (♩=95)

Fred Kern

Second time both hands 8va

MAJOR SCALE PATTERNS

All **Major Scale Patterns** are made up of eight notes in the following order of semitones and tones.

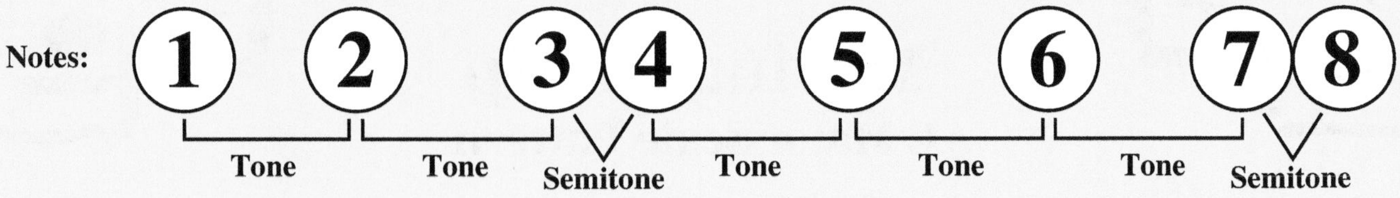

C Major Scale

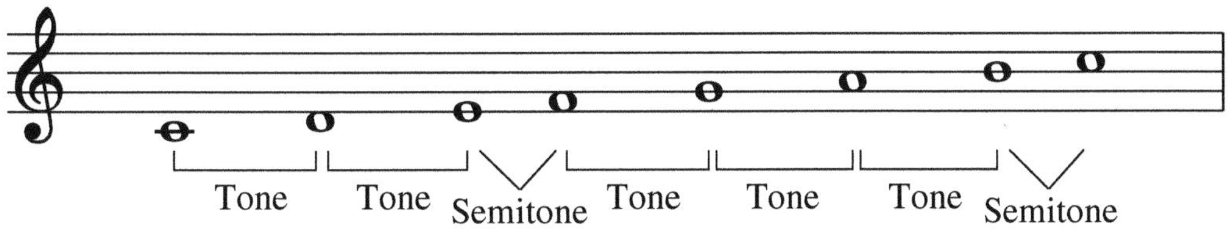

Scale Preparation

Prepare to play a scale by first practising the thumb movements.
Let your arm guide your fingers smoothly up and down the keyboard.

*Allegretto

Katherine Glaser

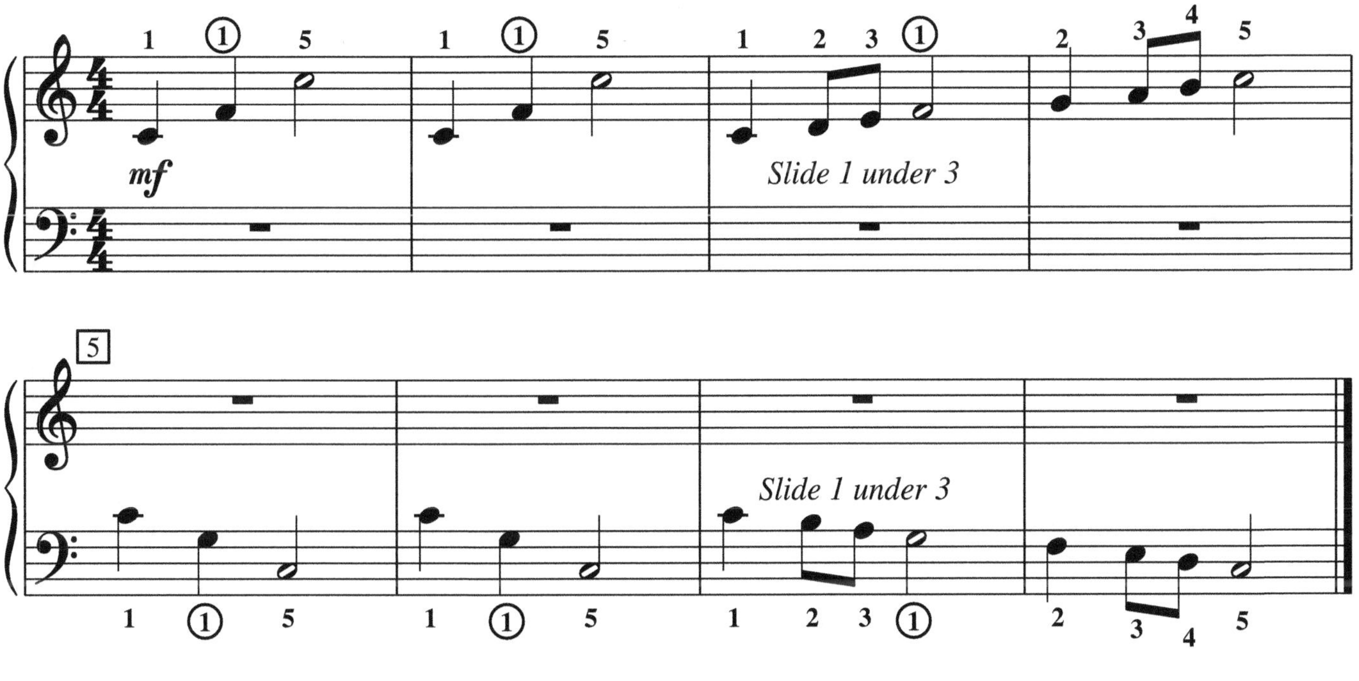

Accompaniment (Student plays one octave higher.)

Allegretto (♩=120)

* *quickly, but not as fast as Allegro*

Moving On Up
C Major Scale Pattern

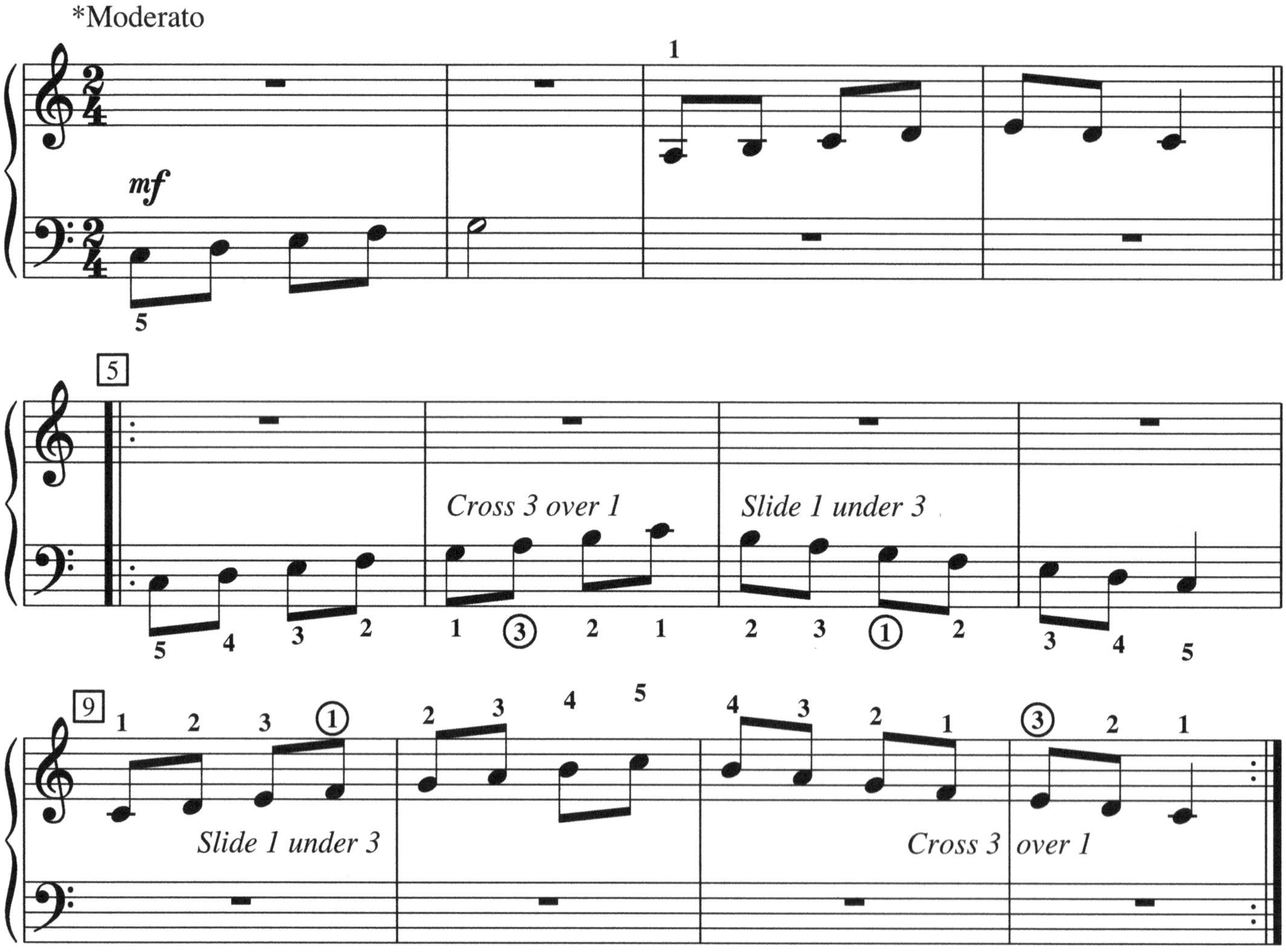

Accompaniment (Student plays two octaves higher than written.)

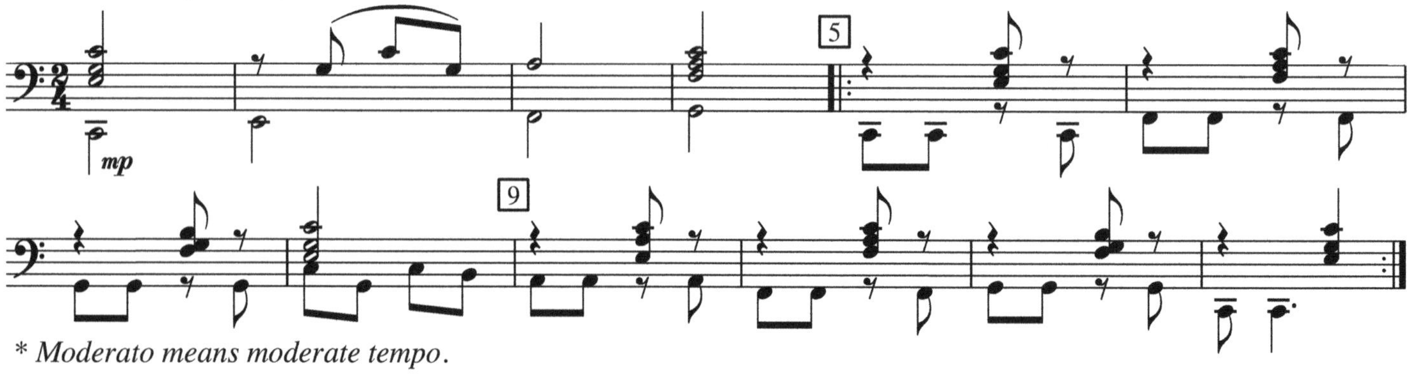

* *Moderato means moderate tempo.*

KEY SIGNATURE

Every piece opens with a **key signature**. It identifies the scale pattern the composer used and tells you which notes to play sharp or flat throughout the piece.

Clap and count:

Calypso Cat

Key of C Major
Key signature: *no sharps, no flats*

Happily (♩=140)

Phillip Keveren

3/8 TIME SIGNATURE

= three quavers fill one bar
= the beat is a quaver

Clap and count:

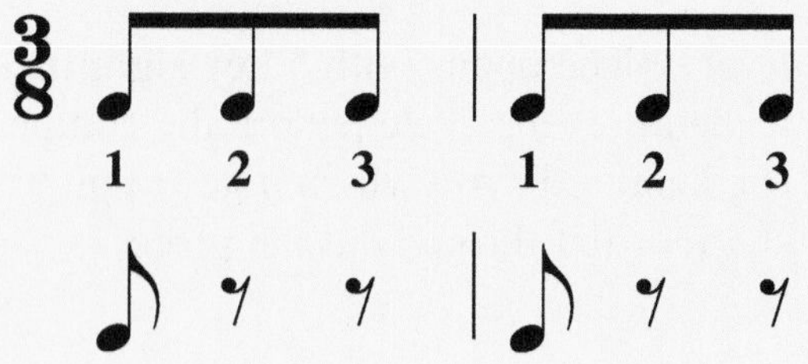

Jig

Irish
Arranged by Fred Kern

Lively (♩. =86)

$\frac{6}{8}$ TIME SIGNATURE

$\frac{6}{8}$ (6 / quaver) = six quavers fill one bar
= the beat is a quaver

Clap and count:

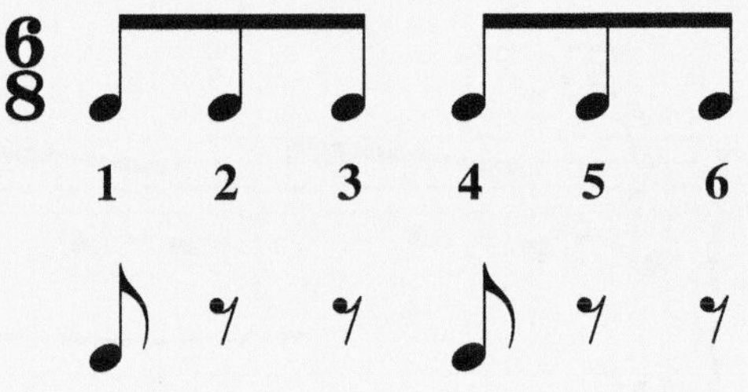

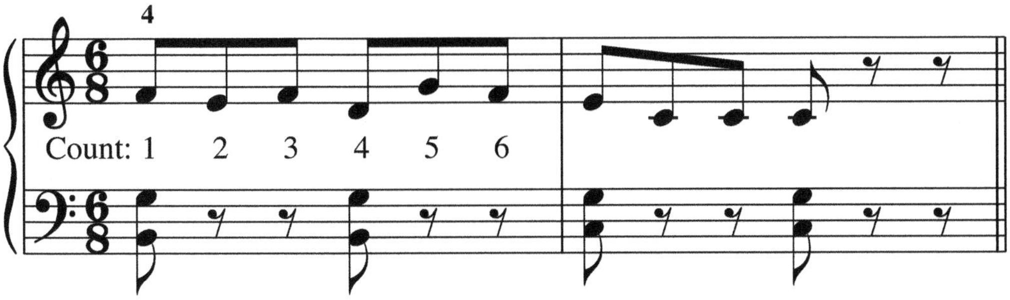

ACCIDENTALS

Sharps (♯), Flats (♭), or Naturals (♮) added to a piece outside the key signature are called **Accidentals**.

Clap and count these patterns:

Two-Four-Six-Eight

Jazzy (♩. =93)

Bill Boyd

2
4
6
8

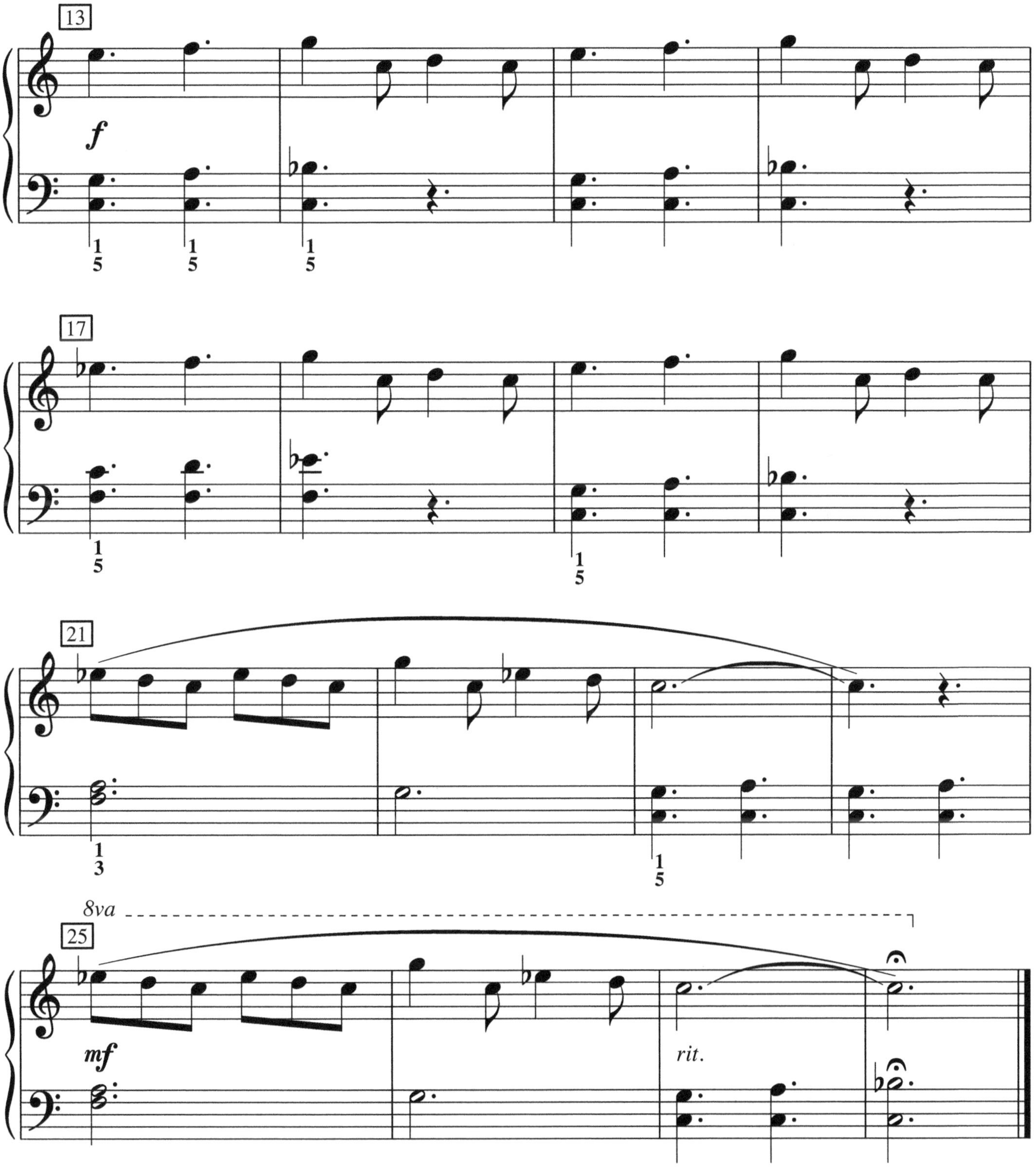
13
f
1 5
1 5
1 5
17
1 5
1 5
21
1 3
1 5
8va
25
mf
rit.

Relative Scales

Every Major Scale has a Relative Minor. It begins on the sixth note of the major scale.

A is the sixth note of the C Major scale. C Major and A Minor are **Relative Scales** because they have the same **Key Signature:** *no sharps and no flats.*

C Major Scale

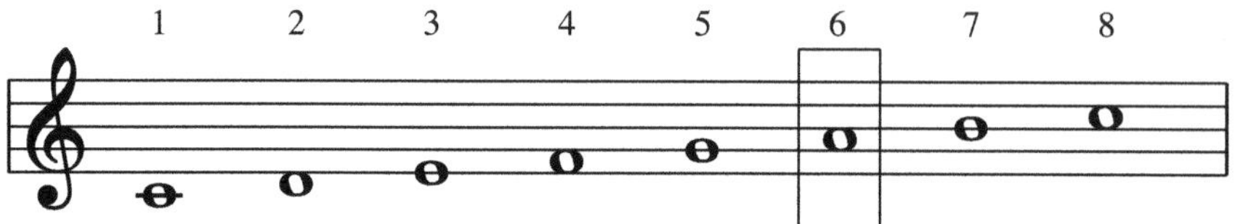

A Minor Scale

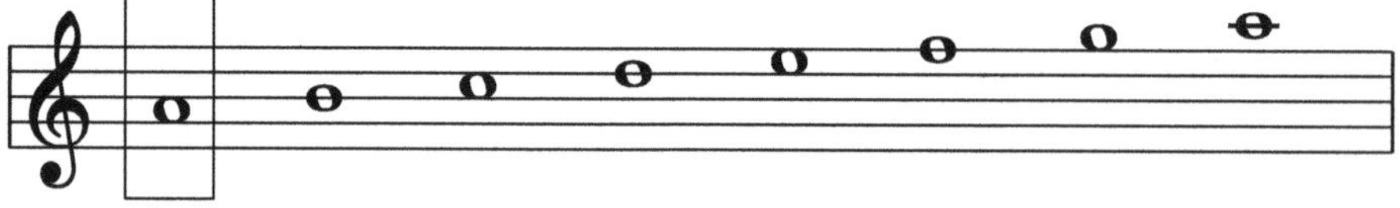

NATURAL MINOR SCALES

All ***Natural*** **Minor Scales** are made up of eight notes in the following order of semitones and tones.

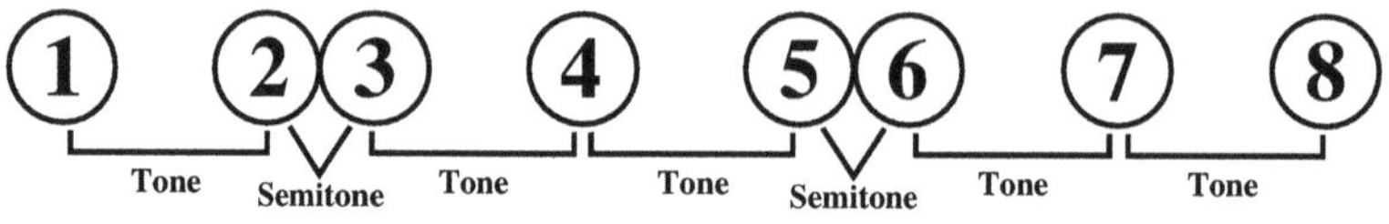

HARMONIC MINOR SCALES

The ***Harmonic*** form of the minor scale raises the seventh note one semitone indicated by an accidental. The A Harmonic Minor Scale has a G♯.

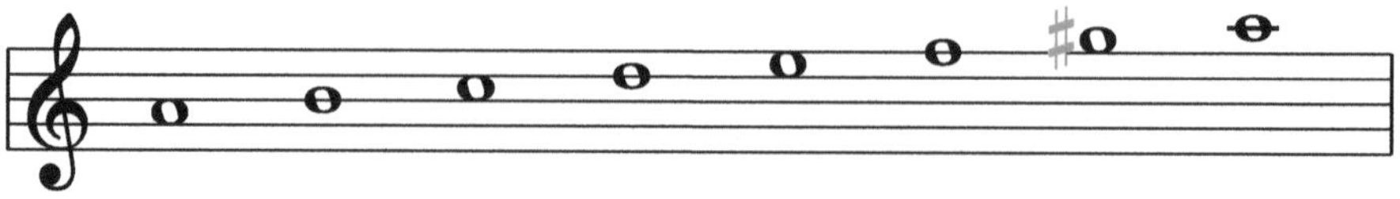

For a quick way to find the relative minor,
move down 3 semitones from the first note of the major scale.

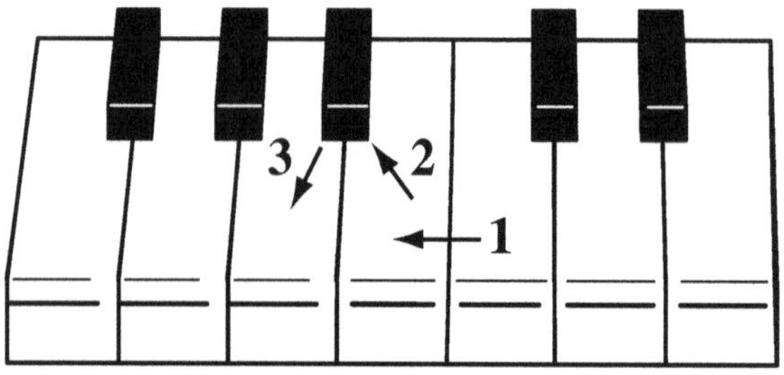

"A" is 3 semitones below "C."

Moving On Up
A Minor Scale Patterns

First, play the ***Natural Minor Scale*** with no sharps.
On the repeat, play the ***Harmonic Minor Scale*** with the raised 7th (G♯).

Moderato

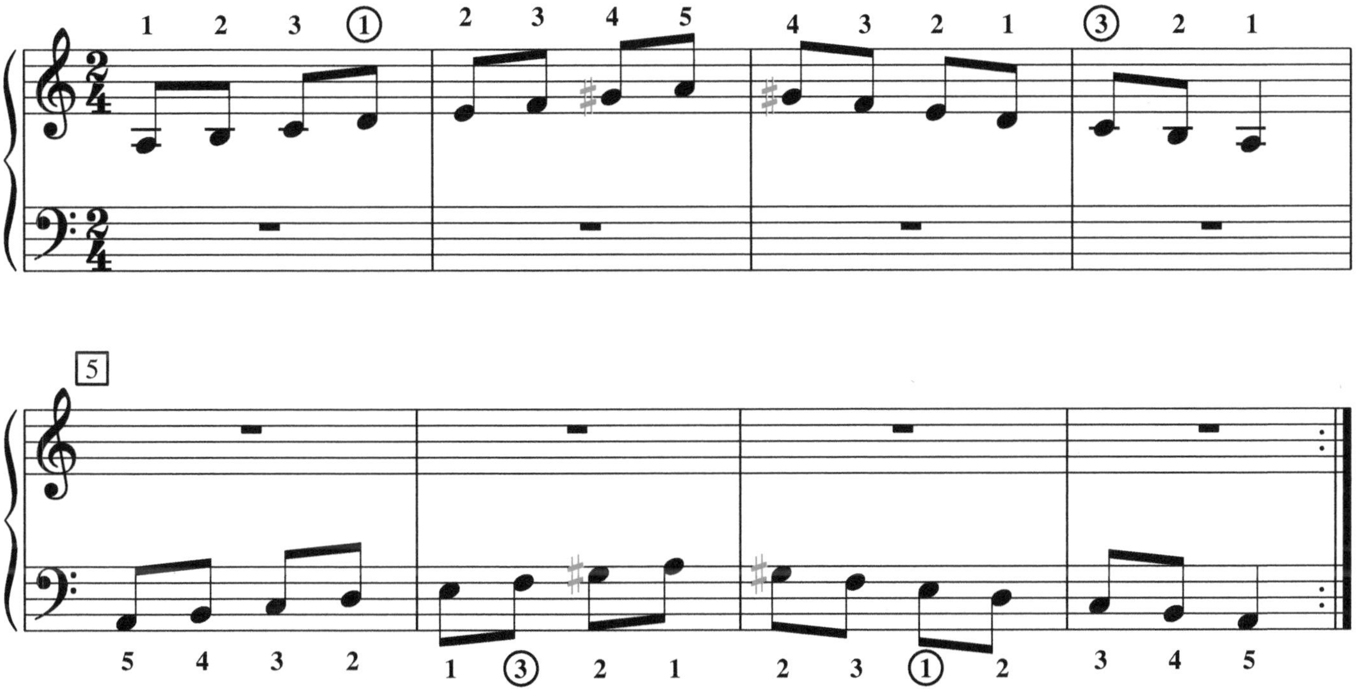

Accompaniment (Student plays two octaves higher than written.)

First, play the natural form with no sharps or flats.
On the repeat, play the harmonic form with the raised 7th (G♯).

Moderato (♩=110)

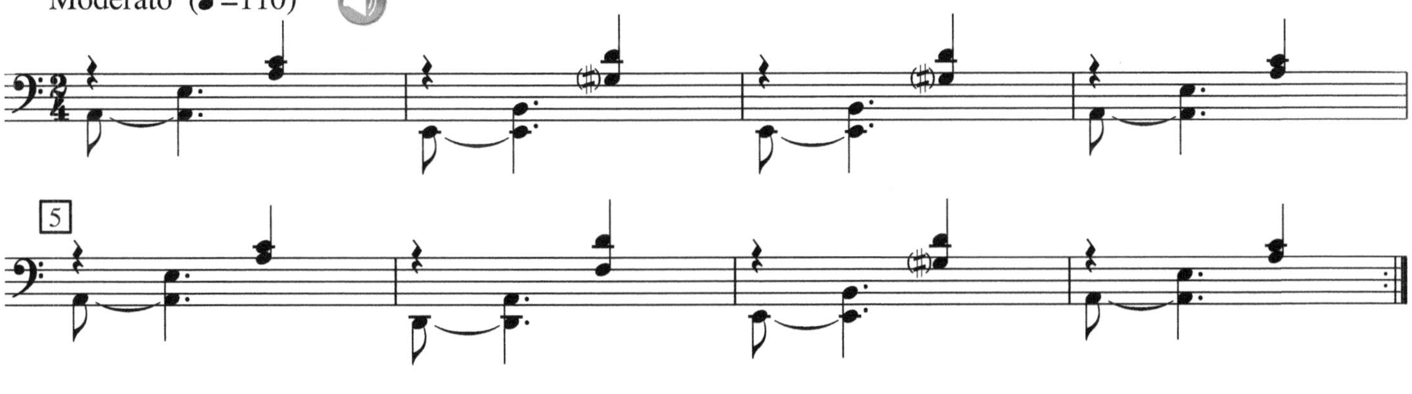

Allegro

Key of A Minor
Key signature: ____________

Cornelius Gurlitt
(1820-1901)
Op. 82, No. 52

Allegro (♩=170)

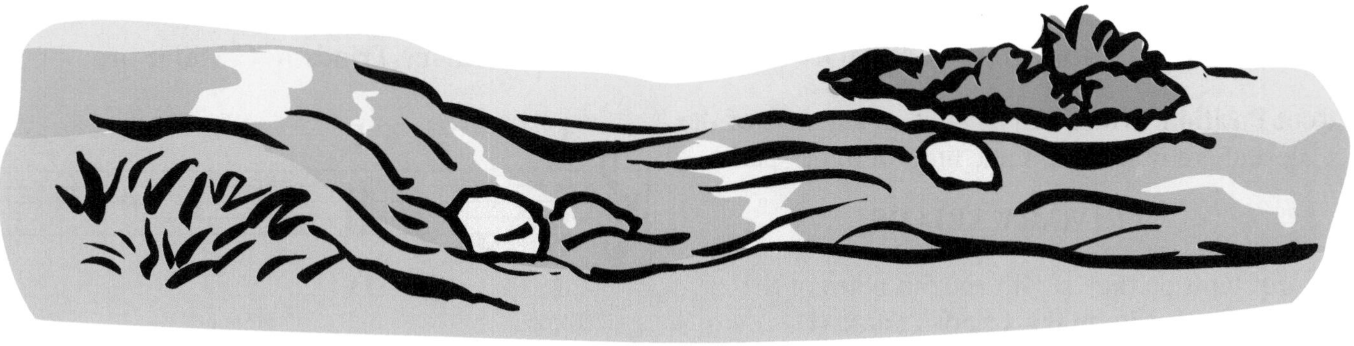

*Etude

Key of A Minor
Key signature: ____________

Ludwig Schytte
(1848-1909)

Flowing (♩. =87)

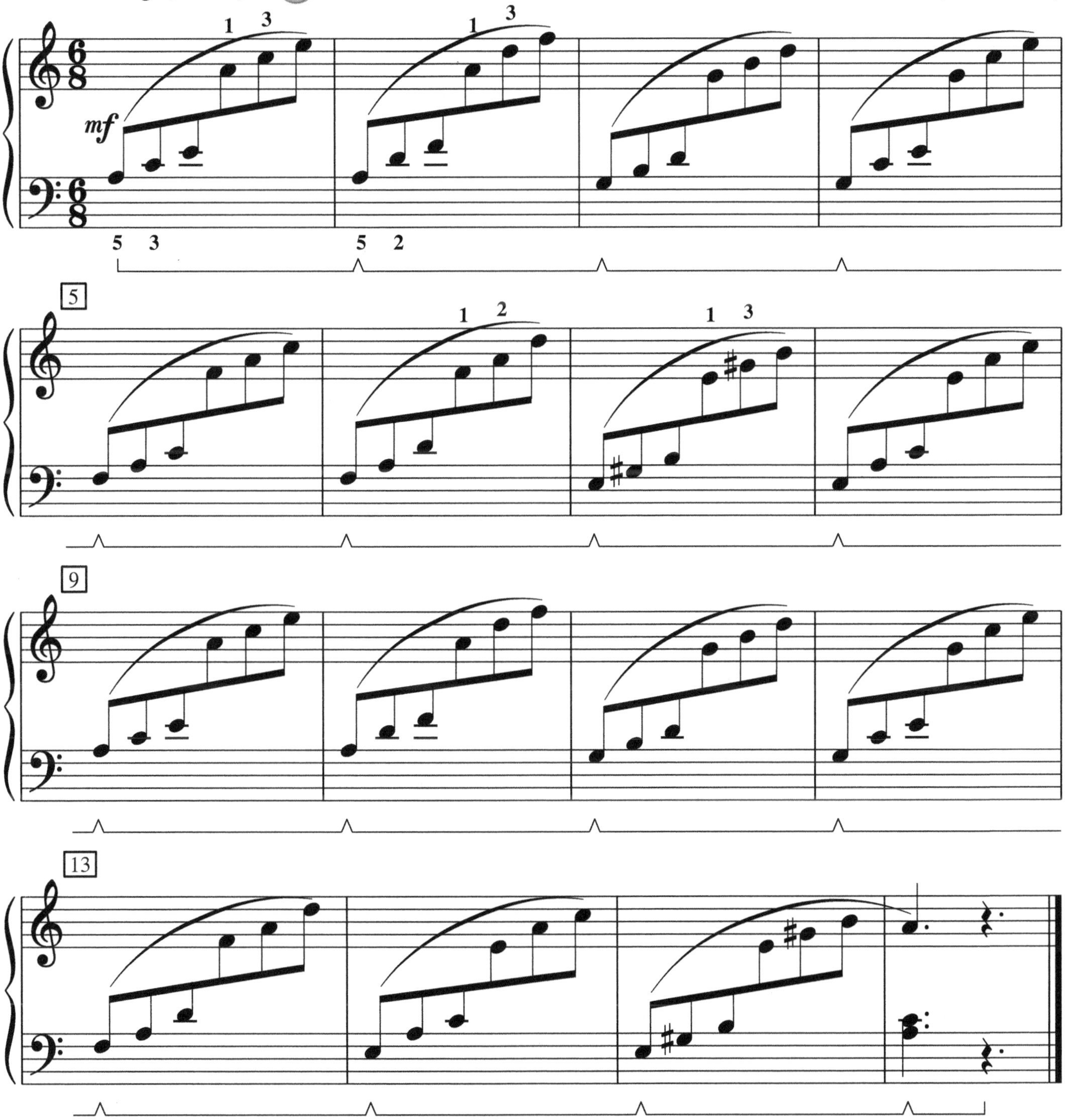

* *Etude means a study or exercise piece.*

TRIADS IN ROOT POSITION

Root Position Triads can be built on any note of the scale and are written on three lines or three spaces.

PRIMARY TRIADS

Chords built on the 1st, 4th and 5th notes of the scale are called **Primary Triads: Tonic (I), Sub-dominant (IV), Dominant (V).**

The Primary Triads in C Major are:

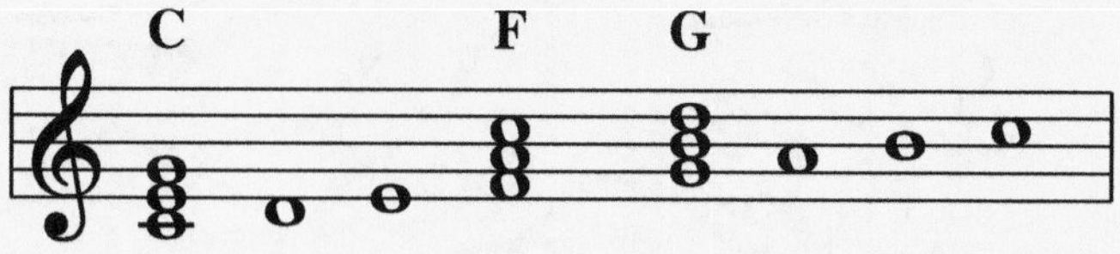

Take It Easy

Chord warm-up in root position

Relaxed

Phillip Keveren

Teacher Solo (Play one octave higher than written.)

Relaxed (♩=130)

PRIMARY TRIADS IN CLOSE POSITION

The notes in root position triads can be rearranged (inverted) to create closer movement from one chord to the next.

The **G7 chord** includes F, the 7th note above G.

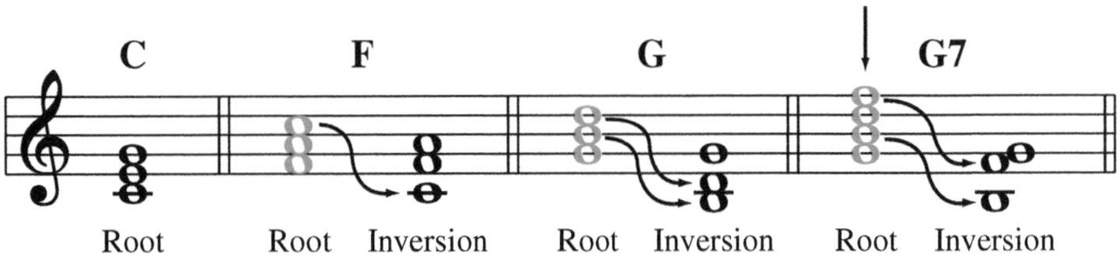

Close By

Chord warm-up in close position

Phillip Keveren

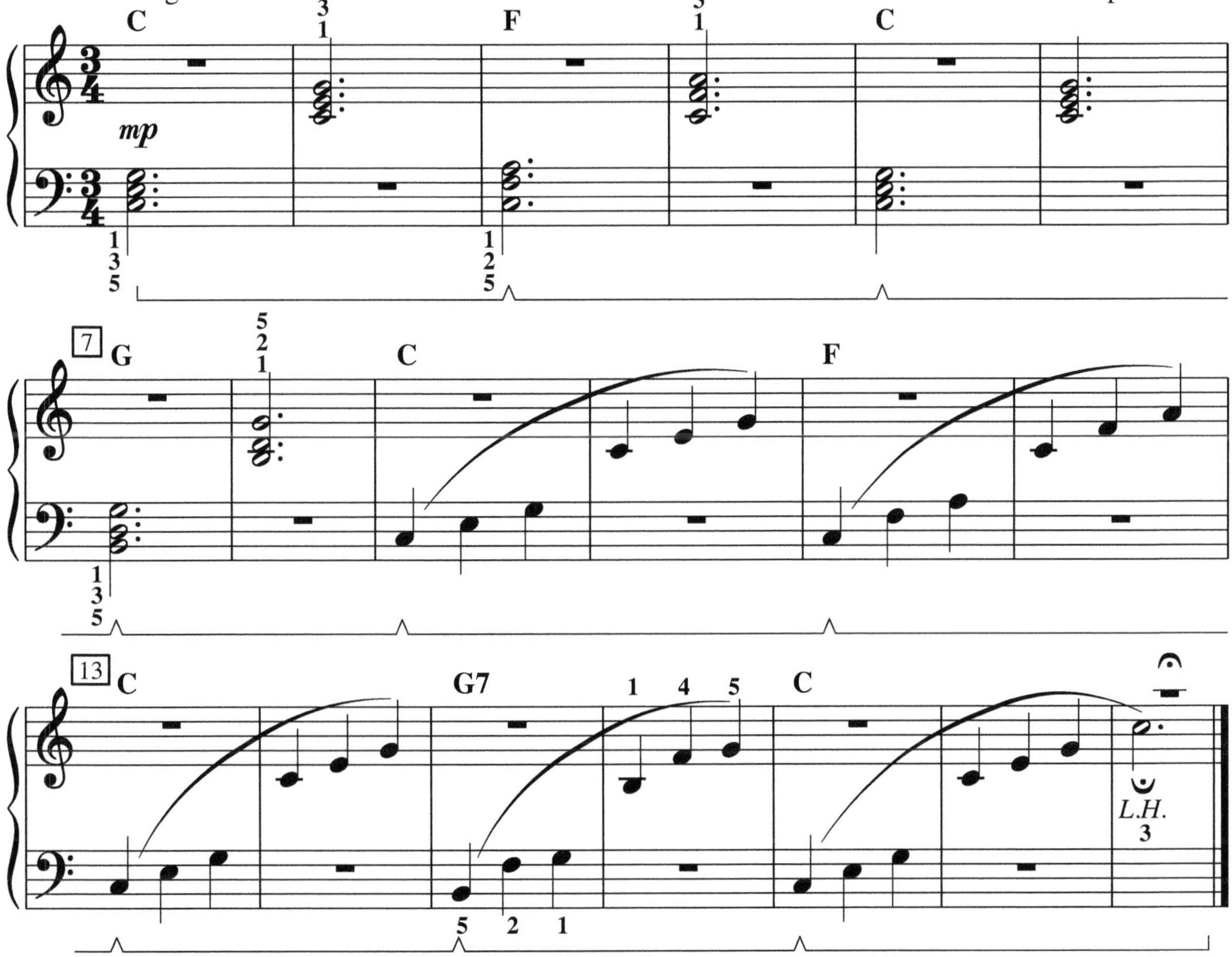

Teacher Solo (Student plays two octaves higher than written.)

My Own Song **Improvisation using *C Major Triads***

As your teacher plays the student part to *Close By,* improvise a new melody in the key of **C Major**.

INTERVAL of an OCTAVE (8th)

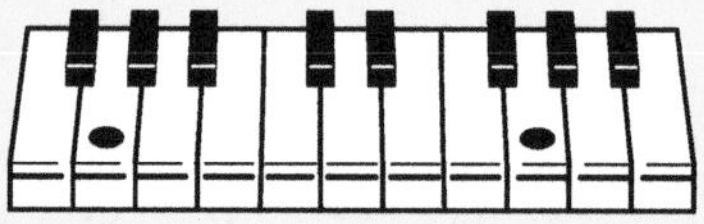

On the piano, an octave
- skips six keys
- skips six letters

On the stave, an octave skips six notes, from either line to space or space to line. Both notes in an octave have the same letter name.

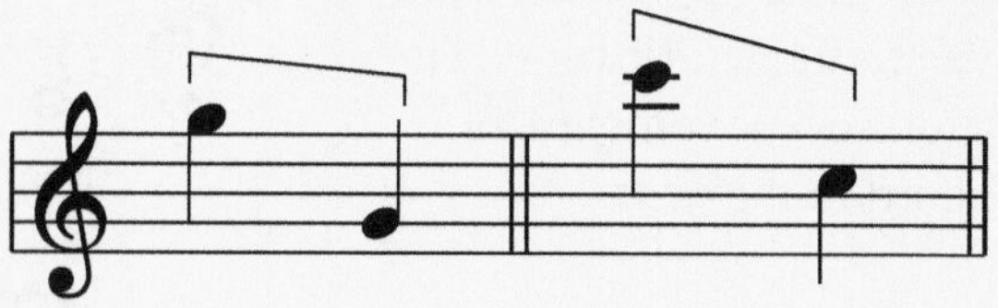

Jumping Beans

Allegro *giocoso (♩=165)

Kreader, Kern, Keveren

* *Giocoso means humorous*

COMMON TIME

C

Common Time is another name for $\frac{4}{4}$.

Relay Race

Carl Czerny
(1791-1857)

Allegretto (♩=155)

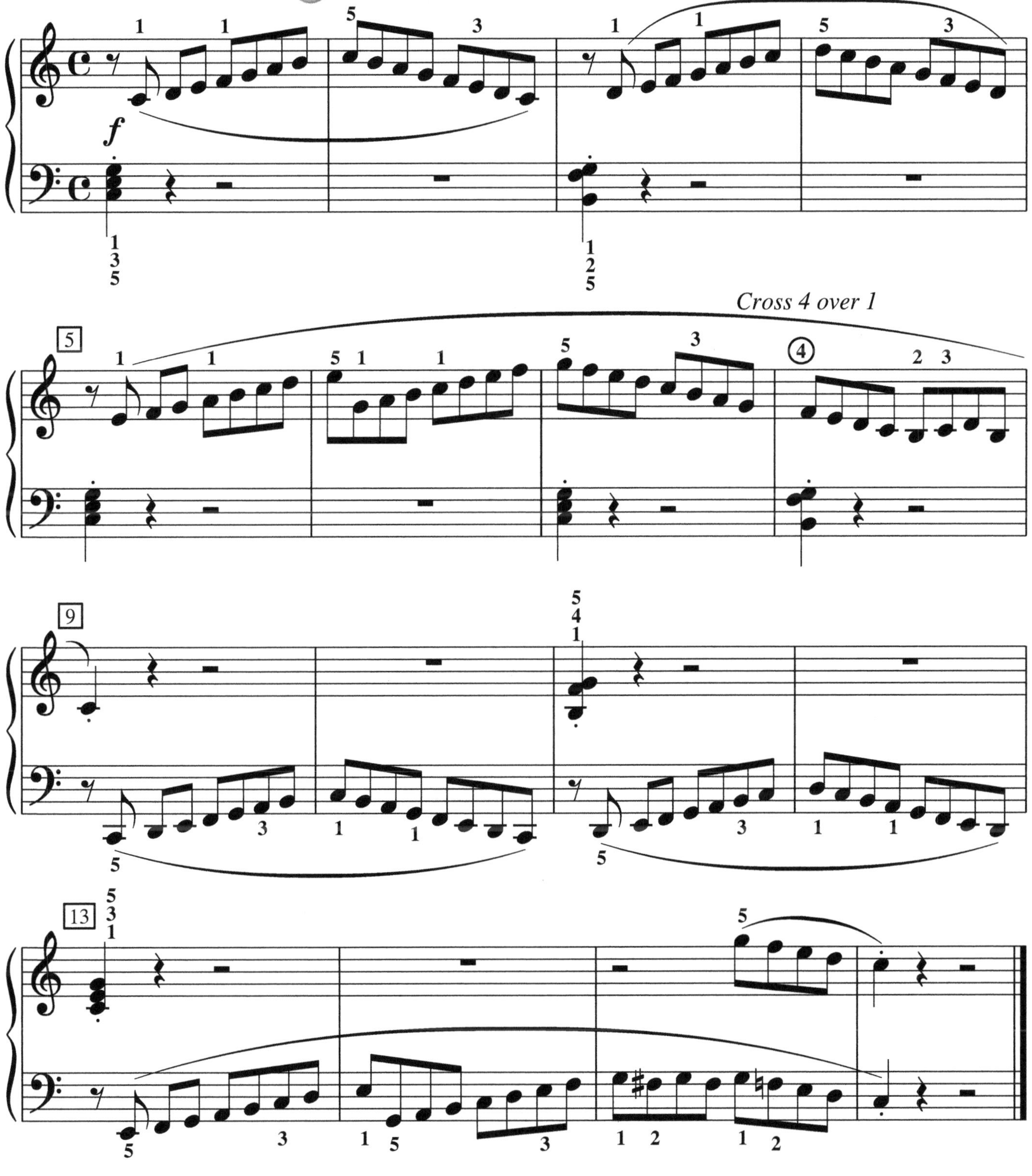

The Primary Triads in **A Minor** are:

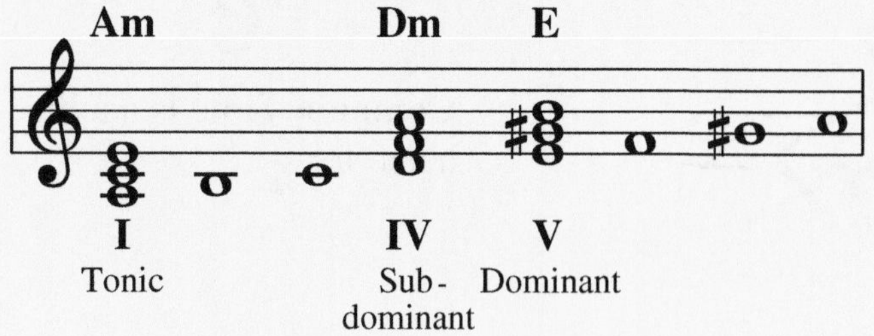

Practise these chords in **close position** before playing *A Minor Tango*:

The **E7 chord** includes D, the 7th note above E.

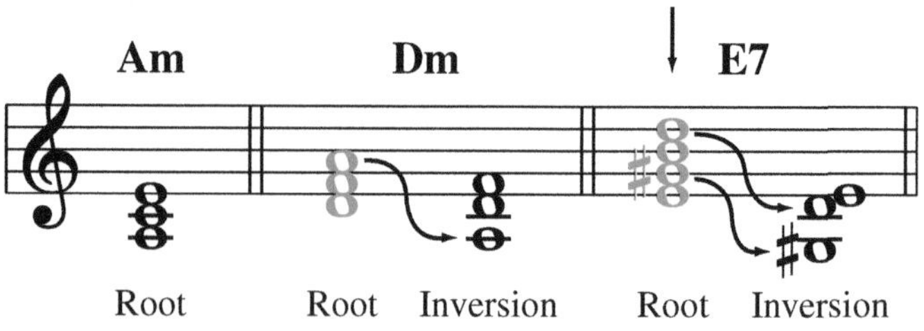

A Minor Tango

Moderato

Phillip Keveren

Teacher Solo

Moderato (♩=120)

My Own Song **Improvisation using *A Minor Triads***

As your teacher plays the student part to *A Minor Tango,* improvise a new melody in the key of **A Minor**.

All The Pretty Little Horses

American
Arranged by Fred Kern

Slowly (♩=94)

Joshua Fit The Battle Of Jericho

Theme and Variations

CHANGING METRES

This piece uses a different time signature for the theme and each variation:

- $\frac{4}{4}$ for the Traditional style,
- $\frac{3}{4}$ for the Classical style, and
- $\frac{4}{4}$ for the Jazz style.

Theme: **Traditional**

Allegretto (♩=170)

Phillip Keveren

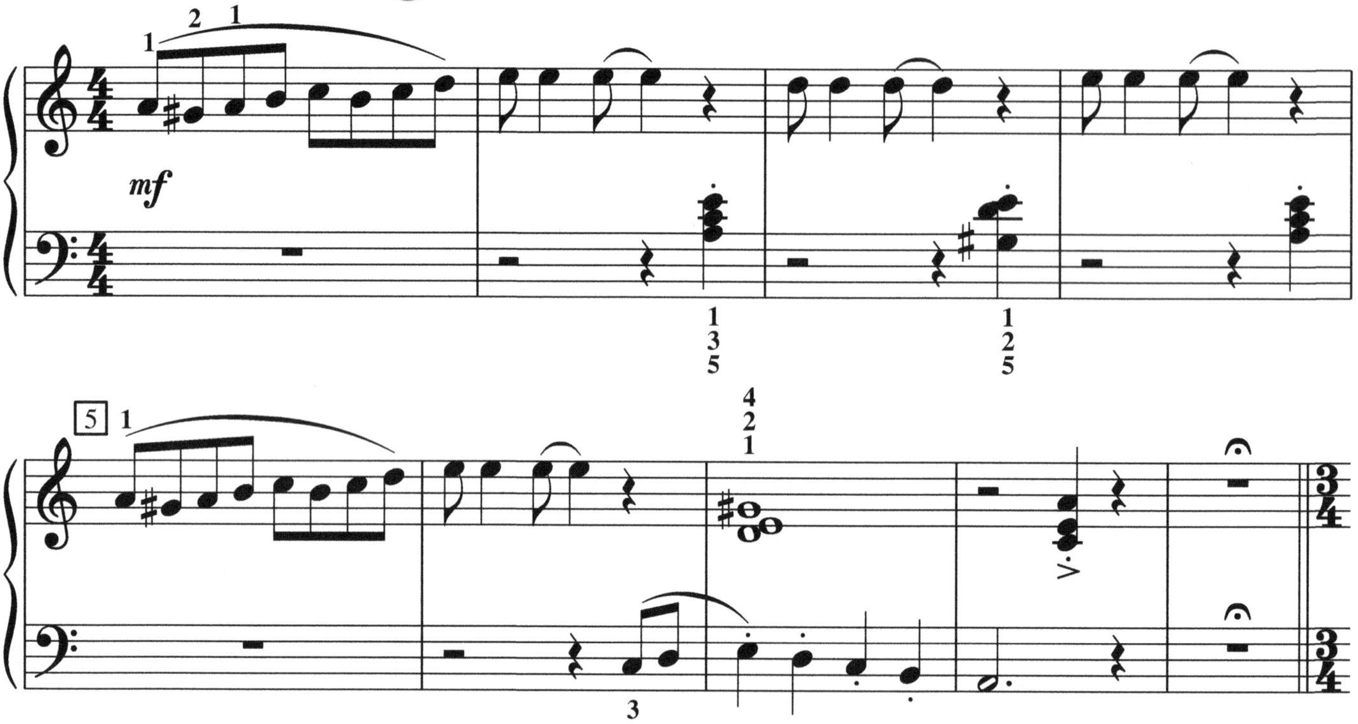

Variation I: **Classical**

Fleeting (♩=185) *1st time both hands 8va*

Variation II: **Swing Quavers**

Laid-back Jazz (♩=150)

G Major Scale Pattern

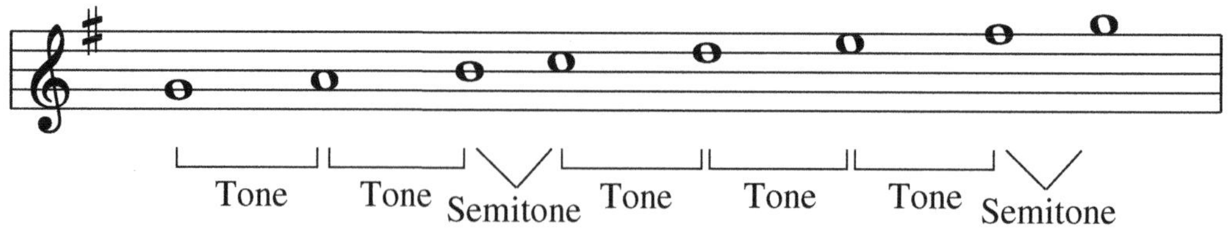

Moving On Up

Key of G Major
Key signature: *one sharp, F♯*

Accompaniment (Student plays one octave higher than written.)

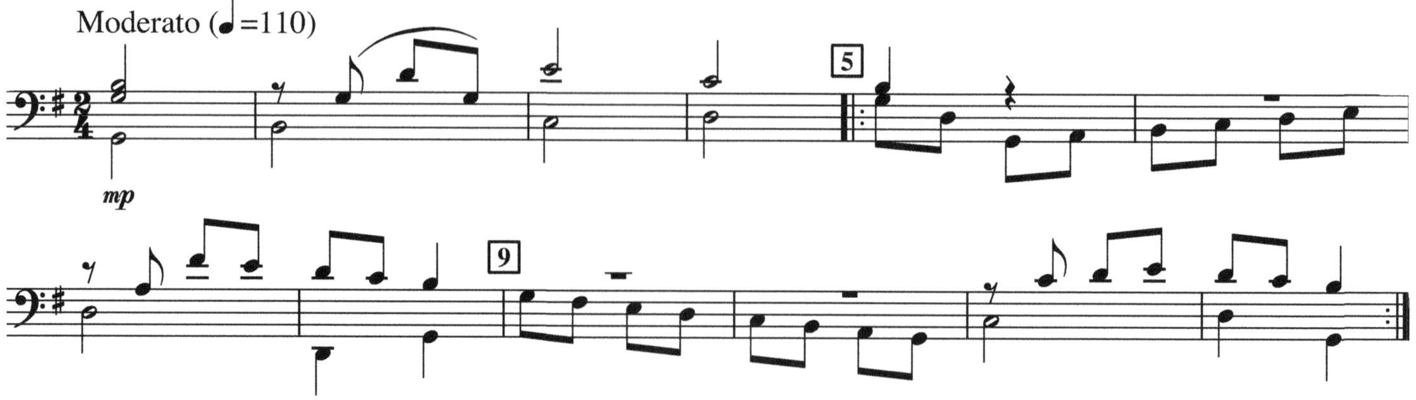

Spanish Dance

Key of G Major
Key signature: ____________

Muzio Clementi
(1752-1832)
Adapted by Fred Kern

* Vivace (♩=180)

* *Vivace means lively.*

CUT COMMON TIME

₵ (2 over a minim) = two beats fill the bar
= the beat is a minim

C **Common Time** has the feeling of four beats per bar.

₵ **Cut Common Time** changes the feeling to two beats per bar.

Clap and count these patterns:

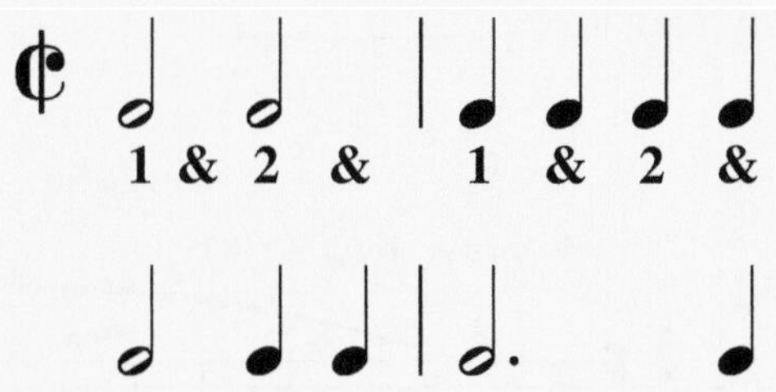

True Blues

Slowly (𝅗𝅥=60)

Bill Boyd

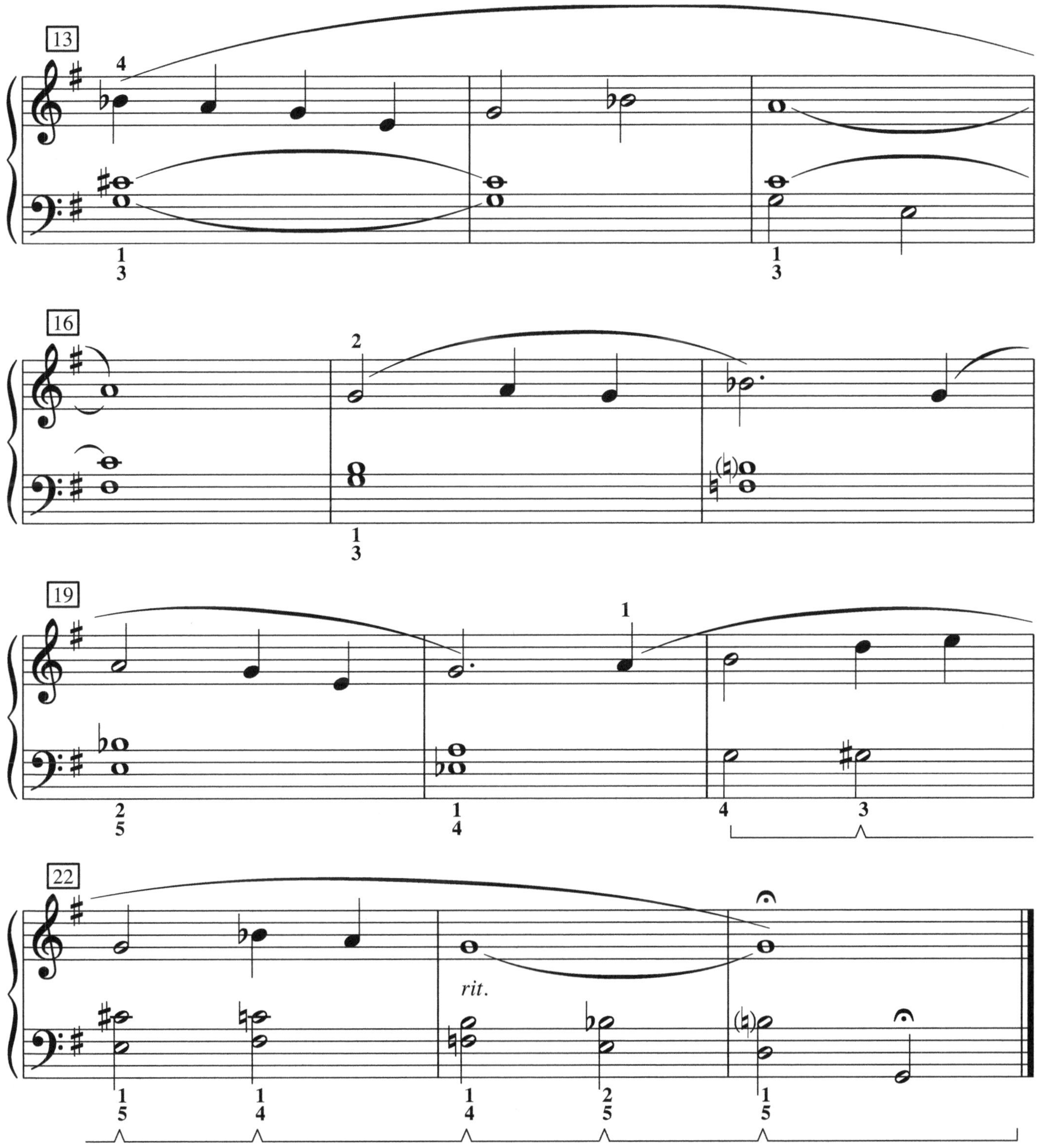
13
16
19
22
rit.

TRIPLETS

A quaver **Triplet** fills the time of one crotchet.

Blues For A Count

Moving along (♩=120)

Bruce Berr

Clap and count these patterns:

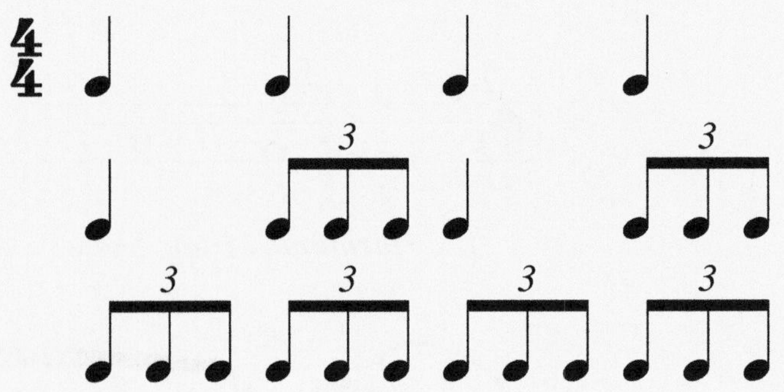

Doo Wop Ditty

Happily, in no big hurry (♩=65)

Phillip Keveren

E Minor Scale Patterns

Natural Minor

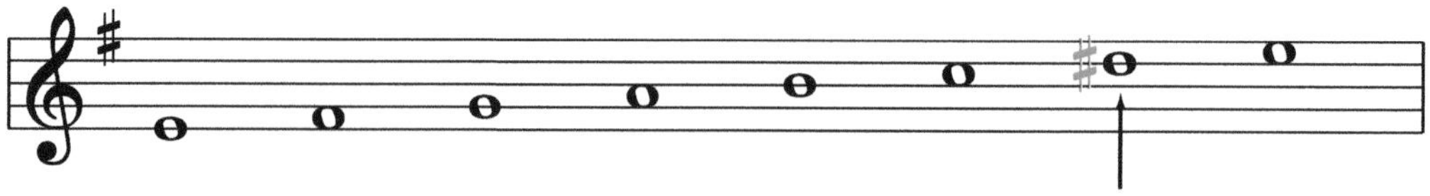

The ***Harmonic Minor Scale*** raises the seventh note by one semitone (D♯).

Moving On Up

Key of E Minor
Key signature: *one sharp, F♯*

First, play the ***Natural Minor Scale*** with F♯.
On the repeat, play the ***Harmonic Minor Scale*** with the raised 7th (D♯).

Moderato

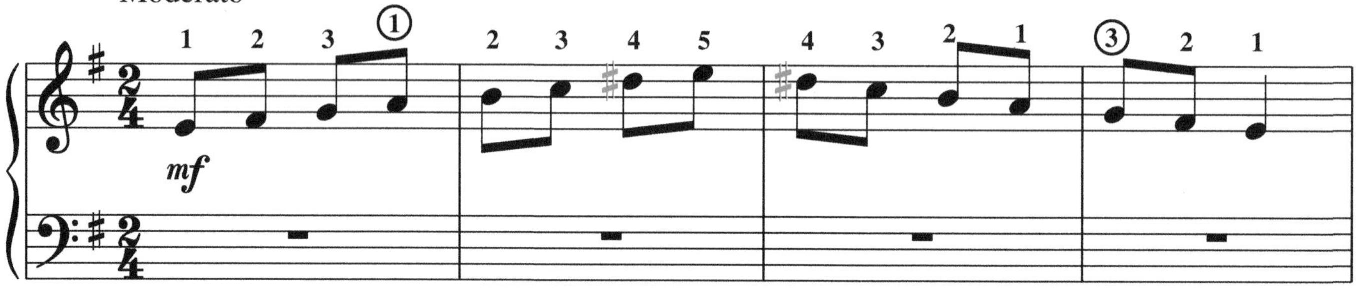

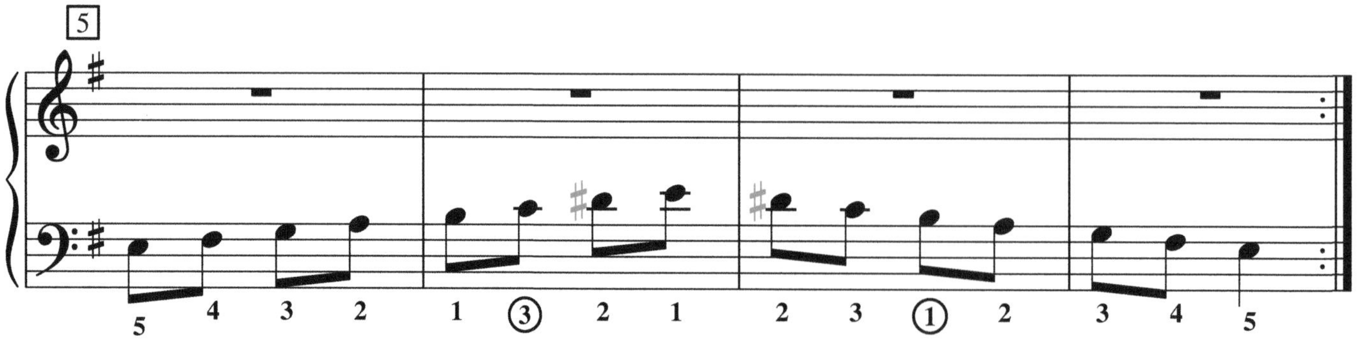

Accompaniment (Student plays one octave higher than written.)

First, play the natural form with F♯.
On the repeat, play the harmonic form with the raised 7th (D♯).

Moderato (♩=110)

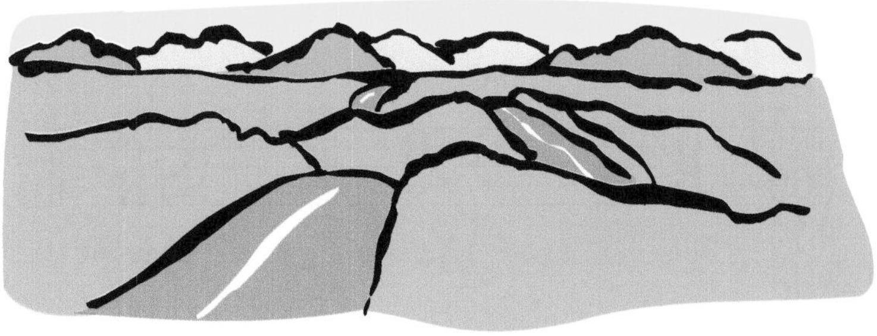

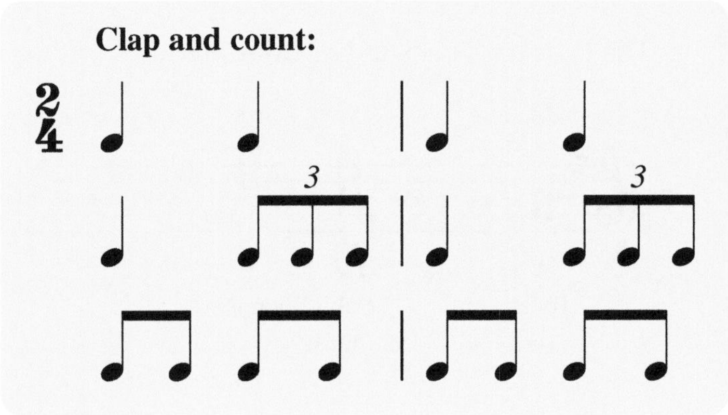

Wandering

Key of E Minor
Key signature: ____________

Adagio (♩=74)

Fred Kern

The Primary Triads in **G Major** are:

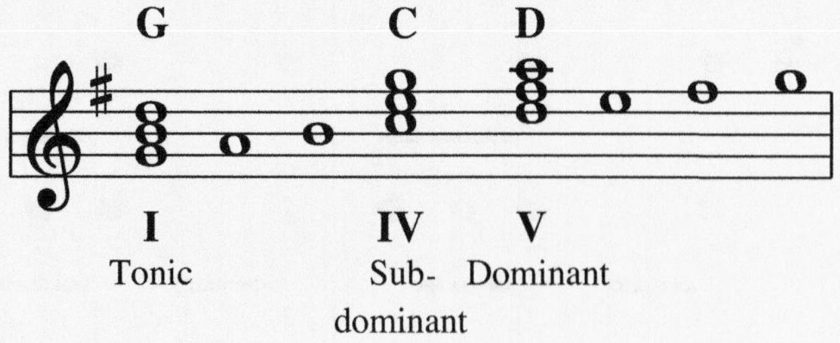

Practise these chords in **close position** before playing *Ready To Rock:*

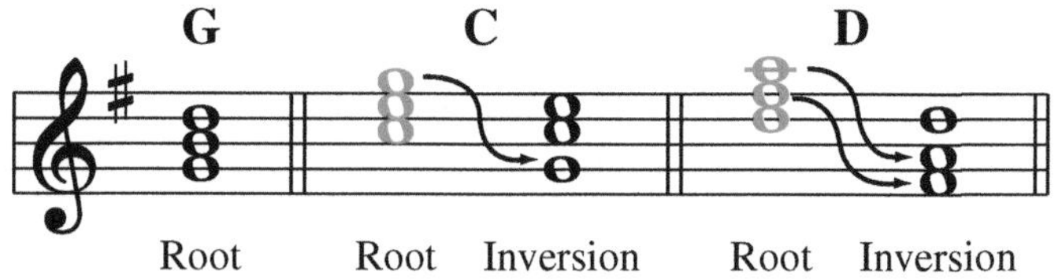

Ready To Rock!

Rockin'

Phillip Keveren

Teacher Solo (Student plays one octave lower than written.)

Rockin' (♩=120)

8va throughout

The **D7 chord** includes a C, the 7th note above D.

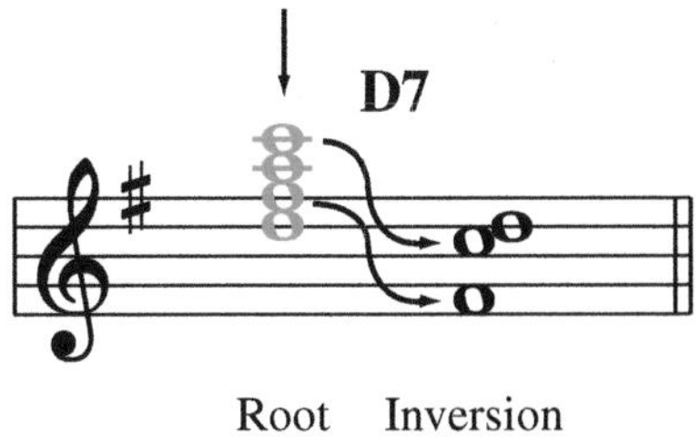

The Bass Singer

Ludwig Schytte
(1848-1909)

Moderato (♩=100)

The Primary Triads in **E Minor** are:

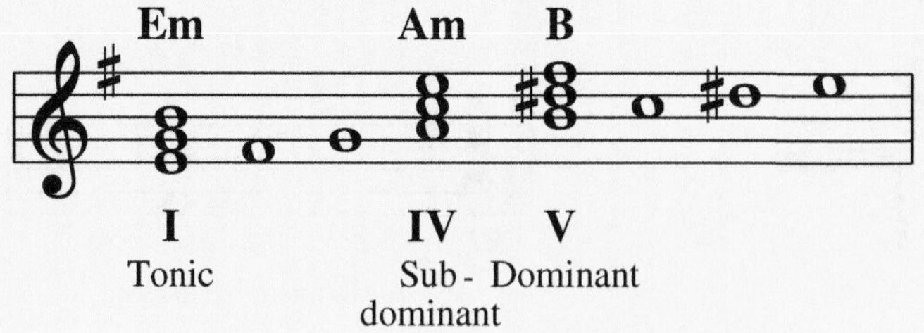

Practise these chords in **close position** before playing *On the Prowl:*

The **B7 chord** includes an A, the 7th note above B.

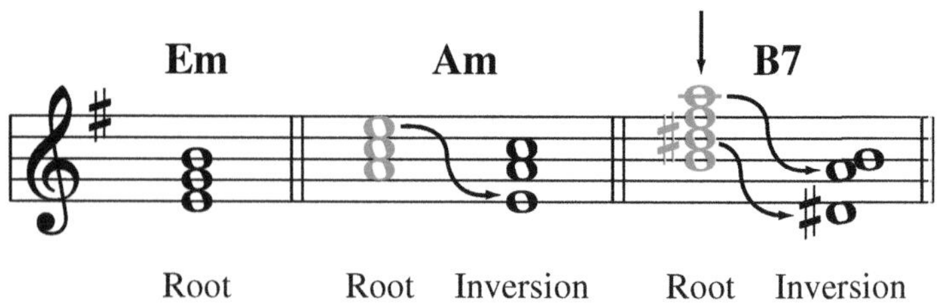

On The Prowl

Cautiously

Phillip Keveren

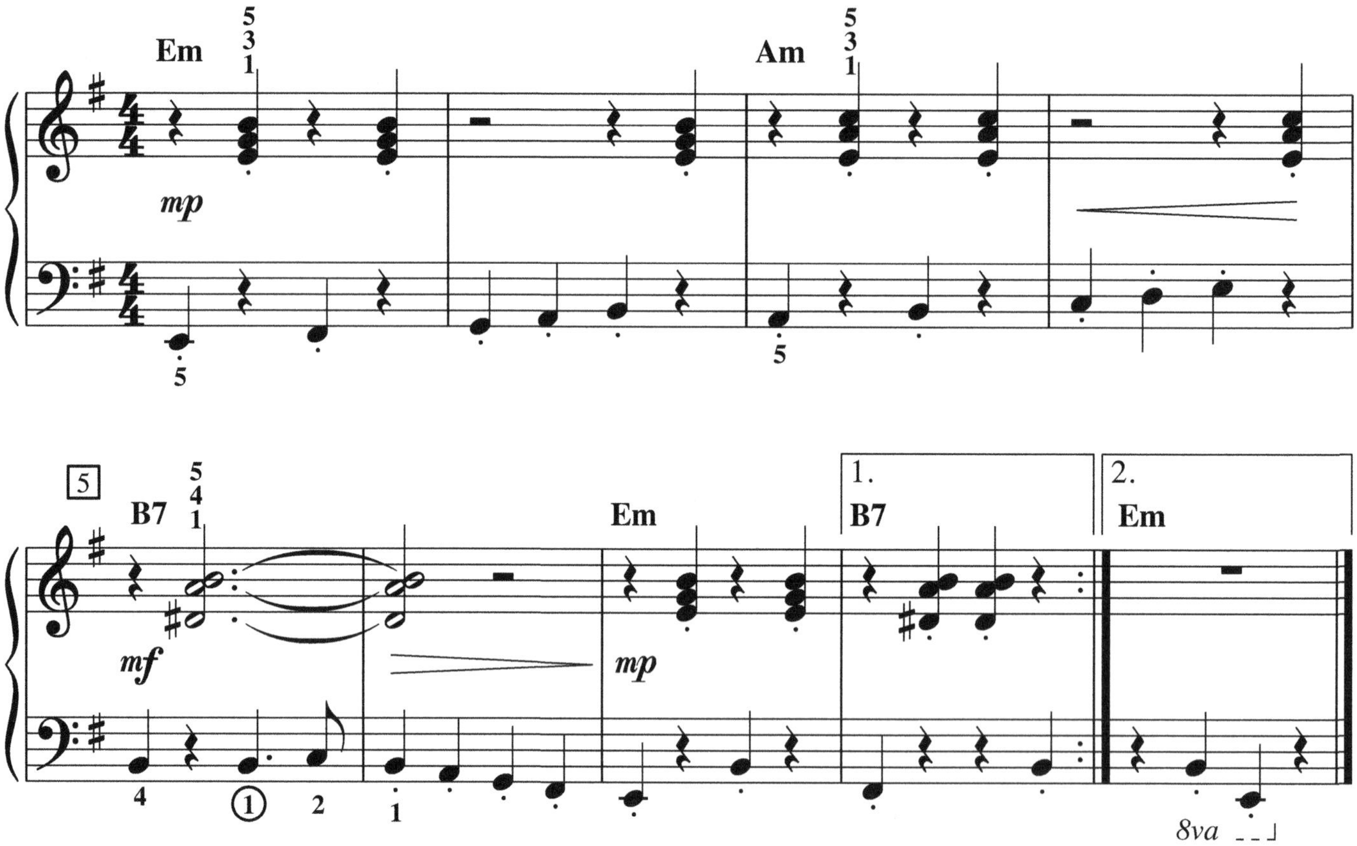

Teacher Solo

My Own Song **Improvisation using *E Minor Triads***

As your teacher plays the student part to *On The Prowl,* improvise a new melody in the key of **E Minor**.

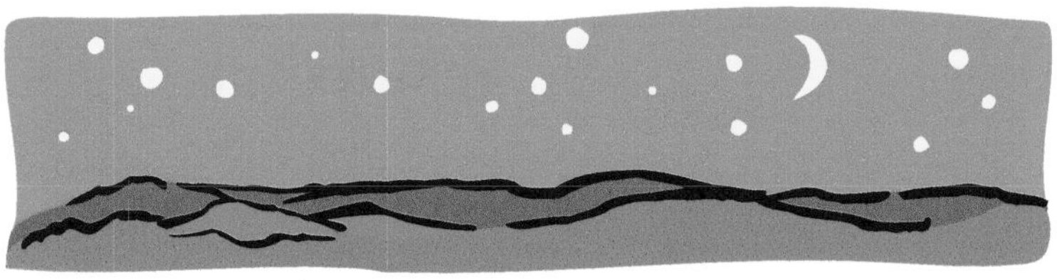

Starry Night

FINGER SUBSTITUTION

Sometimes a phrase extends beyond the range of a five-finger pattern. To keep the sound smooth and connected, substitute one finger for another on the repeated note.

Andante (♩=98)

Italo Taranta

TENUTO

A short line over or under a note means to play **Tenuto**. Give the note extra emphasis, holding it for its full value.

Rhapsody

Allegro (♩=180)

Jennifer Linn

16
8va
mf
p
20
ritardando
24
mf
a tempo
28
31
8va
ff

Longing

Andante *con moto (♩. =35)

Barbara Kreader

** Con moto means with motion.*

Presto

George A.Benda
(1722-1795)
Adapted by Fred Kern

* Presto (♩=170)

* *Presto means fast.*

Allegro

from *Eine Kleine Nachtmusik*

Wolfgang A. Mozart
(1756-1791)
Adapted by Fred Kern

Allegro (𝅗𝅥=120)

21
p
27
mf
33
f
37
42

Instrumental Accompaniments

orchestrated by Phillip Keveren

Audio Track List

	Page	Track # with Solo *practice tempo*	Track # w/o Solo *performance tempo*
UNIT 1			
My Own Song – C Major & A Minor	4	–	1
Rustic Dance	5	2	3
Carpet Ride	6	4	5
My Own Song – G Major & E Minor	7	–	6
Mister Banjo	8	7	8
Morning Bells	9	9	10
Ribbons	10	11	12
UNIT 2			
Scale Preparation	11	13	14
Moving On Up – C Major Scale	12	15	16
Calypso Cat	13	17	18
Jig	14	19	20
Two-Four-Six-Eight	16	21	22
Moving On Up – A Minor Scales	19	23	24
Allegro	20	25	26
Etude	21	27	28
UNIT 3			
Take It Easy	22	29	30
Close By	23	31	32
My Own Song – C Major Triads	23	–	33
Jumping Beans	24	34	35
Relay Race	25	36	37
A Minor Tango	26	38	39
My Own Song – A Minor Triads	26	–	40
All The Pretty Little Horses	27	41	42
Joshua Fit The Battle Of Jericho	28	43	44

	Page	Track # with Solo *practice tempo*	Track # w/o Solo *performance tempo*
UNIT 4			
Moving On Up – G Major Scale	30	45	46
Spanish Dance	31	47	48
True Blues	32	49	50
Blues For A Count	34	51	52
Doo Wop Ditty	35	53	54
Moving On Up – E Minor Scales	36	55	56
Wandering	37	57	58
UNIT 5			
Ready To Rock!	38	59	60
The Bass Singer	39	61	62
On The Prowl	40	63	64
My Own Song – E Minor Triads	40	–	65
Starry Night	41	66	67
Rhapsody	42	68	69
Longing	44	70	71
Presto	45	72	73
Allegro from *Eine Kleine Nachtmusik*	46	74	75

Audio Access Instructions

Visit **www.halleonard.com/mylibrary** and enter the unique access code found on page 1. This will grant you instant online access to both the audio and MIDI files. The audio tracks are available for download or streaming, and MIDI files are available for download only.

For technical support, please email **support@halleonard.com**.